# This Book Belogs To

_____

_____

_____

# I SPY with my little eye someting beginning with......

# A Is for

# Afikomen

# I SPY with my little eye someting beginning with......

# B Is for

# Barbecue

# I SPY with my little eye someting beginning with......

# C Is for

# Cap

# I SPY with my little eye someting beginning with......

# D Is for

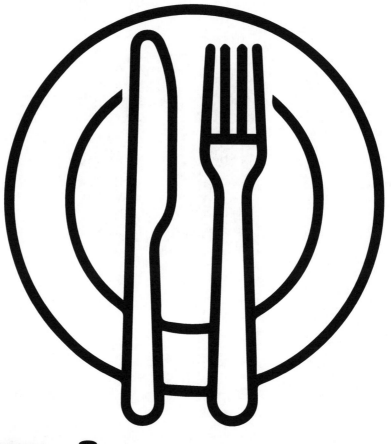

# Dinner

# I SPY with my little eye someting beginning with......

# E Is for

# Egyptian

# I SPY with my little eye someting beginning with......

# F

**Is for**

# Fish

# I SPY with my little eye someting beginning with......

# G Is for

# Grape

# I SPY with my little eye someting beginning with......

# H Is for

# Hamsa

# I SPY with my little eye someting beginning with......

# I Is for

# Isis

# I SPY with my little eye someting beginning with......

# J Is for

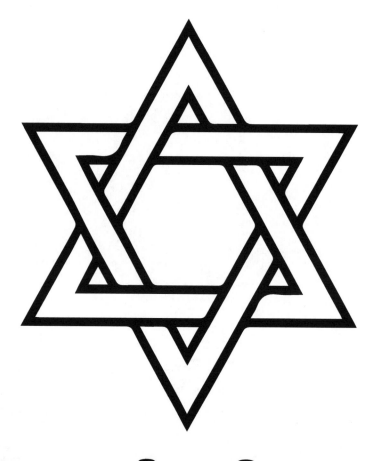

# Judaism

# I SPY with my little eye someting beginning with......

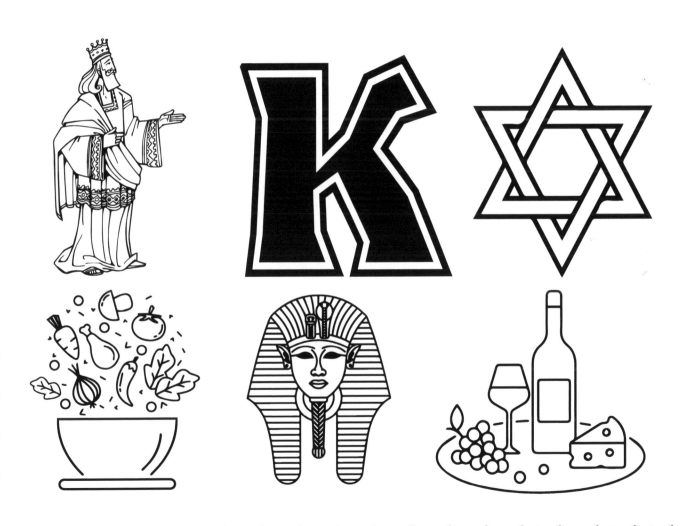

# K Is for

# King

# I SPY with my little eye someting beginning with......

# L Is for

# Lamb

# I SPY with my little eye someting beginning with......

# M Is for

# Menorah

# I SPY with my little eye someting beginning with......

# N Is for

# Nosh

# I SPY with my little eye someting beginning with......

# O Is for

# Olive Oil

# I SPY with my little eye someting beginning with......

# P Is for

# Pharaoh

# I SPY with my little eye someting beginning with......

# Q Is for

# Quill

# I SPY with my little eye someting beginning with......

# R Is for

# Rooster

# I SPY with my little eye someting beginning with......

# S Is for

# Seder

# I SPY with my little eye someting beginning with......

# T Is for

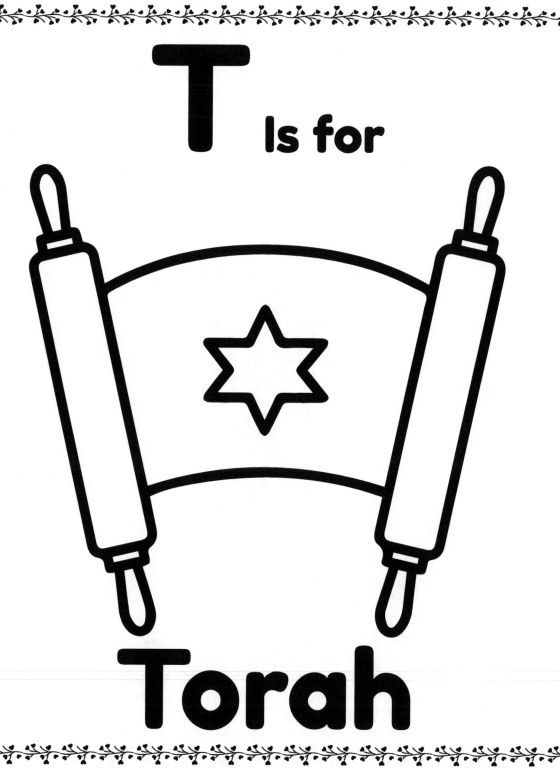

# Torah

# I SPY with my little eye someting beginning with......

# U Is for

# Umbrella

# I SPY with my little eye someting beginning with......

# V Is for

# Vegetables

# I SPY with my little eye someting beginning with......

# W Is for

# Wine

# I SPY with my little eye someting beginning with......

# X is for

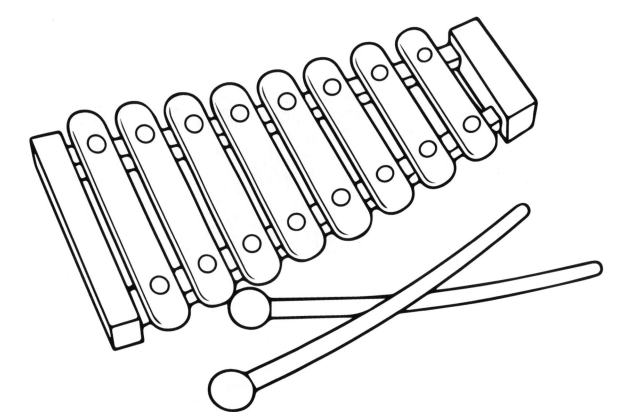

# Xylophone

# I SPY with my little eye someting beginning with......

# Y Is for

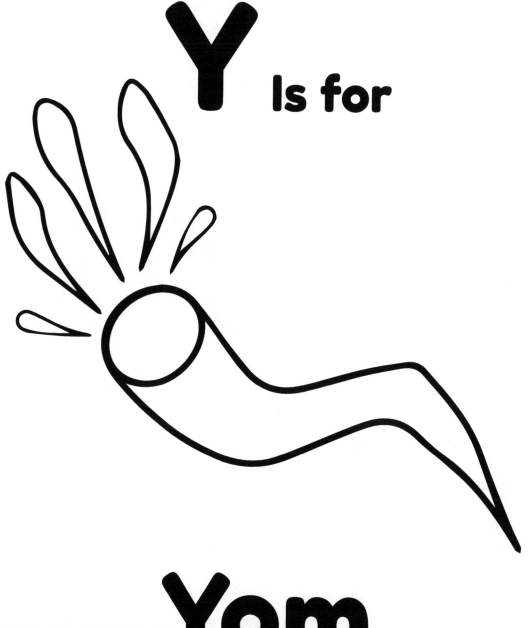

# Yom

# I SPY with my little eye someting beginning with......

# Z Is for

# Zakat

Made in the USA
Middletown, DE
10 April 2022